TERRIBLY NICE PEOPLE

Terribly Nice People

William Hamilton

A BERKLEY WINDHOVER BOOK
published by
BERKLEY PUBLISHING CORPORATION

To A.M.V.H.

Happy Birthday

Bite for Bite — Weekend for Weekend — We'll never know if we're even. We can't count. We can't remember & None of us has ever been able to decide. What do you say — Let's never call it quits & not become terribly nice.

Love,
T.

Special thanks to Lee Lorenz, Stanleigh Arnold, and Richard Theriot

INTRODUCTION

The Chinese invented ink. With it they made paintings emblazoned with words, poems on the subject of the painting, *captions*, if you will, such as cartoonists use now.

I suspect ink is dual-natured. It wants to be words and it wants to be pictures.

I took to ink as a child. I've never liked paint, charcoal, or any other medium as I do ink. I had a wonderful advantage as an ink lover. I grew up in a house left mainly in the last century, a period of ink. Around me was an abundance of the paraphernalia of ink usage: quills, nibs, penholders (one was surmounted by a pea-sized carving of a bull terrier's head with tiny beads for eyes), and old monogrammed silver desk sets, the armory of which included inkwells, penholders, blotters and blotter frames, vials of blotting powder, and other arcane instruments of the inky arts.

When ink was in general use, writing wasn't just the communication of verbal information. You can't use a pen dipped in ink the way you do an IBM typewriter. Ink is too mortal: Your pen starts out overloaded, becomes just right, and then runs out in a rhythm completely oblivious to your train of thought.

In the days of ink, signatures were graceful complexitites (ideally consuming one dip from first stroke to final flourish). Handwriting had to do with manners as well as character, and the independent life of the medium made it more akin to horseback riding than it is to typing.

Words were objects made of ink to be looked at as well as read.

Quaking in a trembling bottle, ink shimmers like a lake under a cold full moon. It spills and spreads like blood. It wants to be both words and images, content and form.

Cartooning may be the last line of an old Chinese race of ink that preserves words and pictures as halves of a single description. In 1470 Shen Chou painted a landscape with this caption:

The big trees exposed to the west wind are losing their leaves.
To be comfortable, I have unfastened the collar of my robe; sitting here, I'm letting the time go by.
Doing nothing, I've turned my back on encroaching autumn. . . . I've not finished my book.
My spirit has gone wandering in the sky . . . who can fathom it?

Not all the ancient Chinese masters added words to their images. Many magnificent artists did not. The same is true of cartooning. I often hear "It doesn't need a caption" spoken as a compliment. Many people seem to feel the captionless cartoon more profound than one above a spoken line.

In Shen's picture you can see most of what he mentions in his poem: the big trees, the daydreaming figure, his unread book and the sky.

But doesn't it charm you to know Shen Chou has loosened his collar? How else can we know he knows he's doing nothing and "who can fathom it?" The poem written in the same ink of which the picture is formed allows us to see the invisible part of the man and the vanished leaves.

WILLIAM HAMILTON

San Francisco
May 19, 1975

"Actually, it's been ages since I read a really good-looking book."

"Oh, I knew it! You had humanist written all over you!"

"Well, this is Andrew—radical economist and dreamboat."

"Gosh. It seems like only yesterday it was model railroading!"

"Of course you're unique! You're unique, I'm unique—everybody's unique!"

"And your eyes—God, your eyes! They're as green as the fifteen hand-rubbed coats of lacquer on my motorcycle!"

"Important? Are you kidding? He's under surveillance, for God's sake!"

"I know it looks kinda screwy, but they probably feel just like we felt
away back on that squeaky porch swing!"

"To tell the truth, I wish I'd been born back before sex."

"Darling organic rural Henry. . . ."

"Oh, Michael—I'm so glad you're a living *artist!*"

"By 'high-powered,' you mean he's rich or smart?"

"*I love you so much I've decided to become a Democrat!*"

"*I warn you, Sara—if you leave me I'll lapse into political apathy!*"

"Emily Dickinson, Leonardo da Vinci, Sir Walter Raleigh, and of
course Queen Elizabeth, Van Gogh, Schubert, Salome, and Joan of Arc:
all very, very great singles."

"God. Who would have thought an old Bloomsbury freak like me would go Aspen!"

"By God, Willkie, you're right! Our affair was made possible by a grant from the Ford Foundation."

"Whenever I see all the pots you've thrown, Nancy, I just want to go home and throw my head off."

"Gee, I haven't thought about him in years. The last I heard he married that little Miss Social Register from Vassar, had three girls, lives in Greenwich, works in the Foreign Exchange Division of Chase Manhattan, golfs in the eighties, and has a cat named Burnt Norton."

"He's enormously creative, which is awful because he's also enormously untalented."

"Harvard really did a number on me."

"You're stuffy. That's nice."

"*Damn it, darling, that's not true—I want and need your feedback.*"

"*I think we have it, sort of sensual-intellectual.*"

"Oh, baking. I love baking—so tactile!"

"'Snag a taxi and go to the track'—gee, Dave—you're just like a good old late movie."

"I'm sorry, Don. You have a fine mind, but Evan has a finer mind."

"She's definitely short-story material."

"I'm so glad you're cynical. Roger was so full of hope."

"Dear Mummy: Just a quick note while Nedsy has me on 'hold.' . . ."

"*I don't know what I want to be, so I've decided just to be parasomething for a while.*"

"He's a writer, but so far he's managed to avoid the drag of publication."

"I just don't know if an Abelard-Héloïse relationship has it for the long haul."

"I've tried chanting, analysis, and religion, but shopping and the beauty
parlor are still really it for me."

"Have you got something a little more . . . feminist?"

"I just love your voice. It's incredibly warm and sincere—honest sounding. I'll bet you could make a pile doing commercials."

"No, there are very big, very real differences. For instance, if you're just living together, you don't have to buy these cast-iron French casseroles at forty dollars a throw."

"Tonight you're not going to talk about flying saucers, the Bermuda triangle, weight lifting, or the esthetics of Ruskin. You're going to talk about marriage."

"*Darling, will you, will you share with me the whole middle-class guilt trip?*"

"Well, Mom and Dad, here she is: Ms. Right!"

"When are you targeting the wedding?"

*"If it's to be other than Lohengrin and a white dress, you'd best see the
Reverend Mr. Hamlin."*

"And whenever we need anything, you know, like food and that, well, we're just going to dance and sing until we don't want it anymore."

"*Mr. and Mrs. Taylor—Mary and I want to see if we can hack marriage.*"

"More or less."

"Hi, kids, I'm here to lay the life-insurance trip on you."

"*This is Henry. We live together, too. Only in our case, I'm afraid we're married.*"

"*Are you really mad, Georgie-Porgie, or are you just role playing?*"

"I just can't believe cockroaches are part of ecology!"

"What if all the inflation and stuff is being caused by a massive, unsus-
pected, and undiscovered, highly sophisticated rip-off at the computer
level?"

"But it is an emergency, Ed: The gold washed off the best china."

"Eleven hundred miles on a BMW, sunrise at Delos, wine and cheese with the fishermen—and I knew I could take Harvard and whatever else life could throw at me."

"Do you ever get the feeling you may have had a previous life-style?"

"Oh, darn, Muff—we would have loved to, but this is the week Porter is
letting his liver regenerate itself."

"But aren't you afraid if we buy a Japanese car we'll be letting down the whales?"

"The living room. Now, if you can, we'd like it Bauhausy, but sort of loungey Bauhausy."

"And here, off the main infant traffic routes, but accessible, is Sara's loom area."

"We did natural with both Amanda and Whitney III, so I think we've earned a rest with this little pumpkinseed."

"Darling! Justin verbalized!"

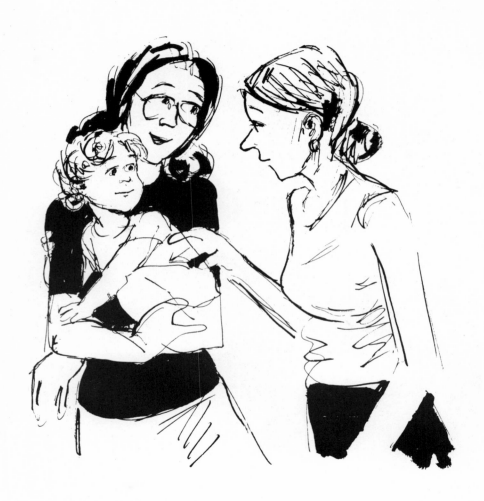

"And this is Jared, born two days after the Ellsberg break-in."

"*Darn it, Ashton, you're old enough to draw your own mandalas.*"

"Granny—you mean the giant was real, real great big—like the phone company?"

"Phil, about little Hugh's camp. Do we want him to learn tennis, French, horsemanship, or survival?"

"Now this, Hughie, is corn—from corn come two of man's most important discoveries: popcorn and bourbon."

"I like the Arnolds—but I like them sort of spaghetti or chicken and this dinner is going to be roast beef."

"Cissy, hi—listen, have you guys eaten? Because we're feeling intensely Szechwanish."

"Now, this is a coming-out party, so I do hope you are establishment journalists."

"*Meg's friend asked for ginger ale. Is he an alcoholic?*"

"Aren't you relatively famous?"

"And you know who else was heavy? Charles Ives! Charles Ives was very, very heavy."

"Yes, it has a nice nose. Sort of aquiline."

"Oh, come on and stay, Addingtons—I'm just going to throw together some convenience food."

"Hell, I'd known this bum since the Selma March. But I didn't land him
until Dump Johnson days."

"Oh, Tina—I love the tux—so decadenty!"

"But maybe you've already seen our house—it's on a tour."

"I'm in publishing. In what are you?"

"For heaven's sake, Amanda, at least be honest with yourself. I was into bluegrass back when you were still on Vivaldi."

"Gosh, Ted, has it been that long? I got over my owl thing ages ago."

"Now, Cathy, will you lay on us a microencapsulation of our last session?"

"They have a bigger apartment, but I think we are bigger people."

"Damn it, Constance, I am not holding anything back! That happens to be all I know about sex."

"En fait, nous sommes aussi de *Kansas City*."

"Christmas cards: Do we want holy, snooty, or groovy?"

"With their *money, they were bound to win.*"

"Hey! 'Made in U.S.A.'"

"In eight months you two will have the strongest architectural statement
in the Hamptons."

"The answer is yes, I have *noticed how many people your age have suddenly made it. I've also noticed how many even younger than you have
already made it.*"

"Here you are. Aries—don't drink so much, stop trying to dominate conversations, more thoughtfulness at home. Be more practical. Try to make more money."

"Why, this breakfast—it's, it's handmade!"

"Look at it this way—poverty is a tax haven."

"Porsches, deep tans, real leather, intellectuals—I'm sick of the whole bit."

"You got into abstract expressionism too late, you went op too late, you were the last into pop—what makes you think it's time to switch to porcelain birds?"

"Do you think you would have tried to oppress me if it had been your money we lived off?"

"Suddenly I'm older than Prince Valiant."

*"Darling, I understand the male Anglo-Saxon is basically built for war.
But don't you think you could be satisfied with just a power trip?"*

"We can't afford anything real, but you are one of our reproductions."

"Just think. If we lived in the People's Republic, we'd probably be weaving these things."

"Honestly, Sigrid, I just can't get over your signed graphics."

"What does it mean? I'll tell you what it means. It means they're loaded."

"They're nice enough, but I wouldn't exactly call them life enhancing."

"I wonder if everything's all right with them. That dip just wasn't Nancy."

"Isn't it ironic? People that insecure living in a designated landmark?"

"*Very Che Guevara.*"

"Bite for bite, drink for drink, weekend for weekend, we're even—what do you say we call it quits?"

"Oh, rats, Muffy—Thursday the ninth is the night we expose the kids to Mahler."

"The way I had it planned, about now we'd be splitting our time be-tween a big apartment and a Corbu house in the south of France."

"'Bye and thanks for a lovely time. Your marriage looks viable."

"I've had all my minimum daily adult requirements—except bourbon."

"Look—public school's not going to kill them—in fact it may give them a certain panache!"

"'Can I please have some money?' 'Can I please have some money?' This kid is getting worse than Yale."

"All right, don't do your homework—but don't expect to ever see your face in a Scotch whisky ad!"

*"This American family has made about enough of its own fun tonight—
let's let CBS take it from here!"*

"You kids are lucky—when we were your age we had to eat processed ice cream and watch TV."

"*I'm proud of you, Stanley, very proud. And I'm proud of me, too. Don't forget to dry.*"

"She uses her maiden name, charges me for child care, and no more waffles on Sunday."

"Daddy, what was it like back before there were any real problems?"

"It may interest you to know touching, caressing—tactile displays of affection—are what make elephant families so damn happy!"

"How did I guess you were a lawyer? Simple—everybody is a lawyer."

"Nancy, there's no dinner! Guadalupe called Mr. Chung a sexist and somehow he found out she is a scientologist and he won't have anything to do with potatoes peeled by scientologists. So now she's yelling, 'Bigot!' and he's calling a priest."

"Are you still doing whatever it was you didn't want to do in order to do what you did want to do?"

"Oh, excuse me, Mr. Howland. It's just that when Phil said, 'Brilliant Boston Brahmin lawyer,' I was hoping for something, you know, Elliot Richardsonish."

"*You're a lawyer? That's funny—you come on sort of creative.*"

"I never remember; did we first meet at the march on the Pentagon or the
Maryland Hunt Cup?"

"I suppose I sound hopelessly out of it, but when you say 'flash,' do you mean in the sense of 'recall' or in the sense of 'barf'?"

"The Columbia takeover? Oh, I'm sorry. I presumed you were reminiscing about the Harvard takeover."

"Aren't you somebody's lawyer or dentist or something?"

"Excuse me, I couldn't resist: Dr. Steinberg, Nobel Prize for physics,
Fifi of Gulnare, Best in Show, Darien, Connecticut."

"Let's see. You're not Peter Bogdanovich and you're not Studs Terkel.
Paolo Soleri? Robert Stone? Charles Schulz? Francis Ford Coppola?"

"It's so nice when summer friends work out."

"*I think things are just plain gloomy enough without reading* The Gulag Archipelago."

"Heavens, no, Solange. The Junior League and the Little League are completely different."

*"Well, that just shows how behind the times I am! I thought a beard
meant creative or naval."*

"Frankly, no. I don't give a good god damn what you think about détente!"

"Hey! What the hell are you cooking? This is The Joy of Sex.*"*

"It's Dudley III! He's somewhere in the wall system!"

"I did not say you looked Byronic. I said you looked moronic."

"Dr. Gold explained why you—I'm a stress seeker."

"Stockhausen does not stink. You stink."

"How do I know you mean it this time? How do I know this isn't just a
strong technical rally?"

"Is this going to be another one of those narrations about me being a total flop?"

"Well, is this it? The terminal argument?"

"I don't know—it seemed like such a real marriage—I mean we even had a subscription to the National Geographic!"

"I haven't just thought about your weaknesses, Peter. I've thought about your strengths, too—and that's why I'm leaving."

"It's not just the béarnaise—it's us!"

"Now do me a favor. Don't ever again go on about how amicable our divorce is."

"Sure it was painful—but what the hell, out of it came his screenplay and my novel."

"Just a goddamned minute—you don't get three years of my life and the
Dietrich Fischer-Dieskaus."

"I've gotten a divorce. I'm living with a good-looking young actress and I'm doing some things I think might be synergetic with what you're doing down at the Environmental Protection Agency."

"We met at a divorce seminar."

"Thanksgiving's about the only time I feel right about being married to that turkey."

*"Basically, all your nations—and this includes Communist China—
would rather be Los Angeles."*

"We try to keep up. Last week we saw a pornographic movie and this week we're taking in a garage sale."

"Goodness! I had no idea intellectuals ate ice cream!"

"The way we dressed, what we read, how we danced—everything about us is coming back—except, of course, us."

"It seems like only yesterday I was OK, you were OK."

"You're leaving out one thing, Frank—Asia."

"*Château Figeac is dynamite wine. Château Ducru-Beaucaillou is dynamite wine. Château Lascombes is dynamite wine. Château La Mission-Haut-Brion is dynamite wine, and Château Beychevelle, Ned, is dynamite wine.*"

"Through thick and thin and bull and bear,
good old Martha was always there,
even back in '47
when I had that little 'affair.'"

"*Frankly, analysis hasn't helped. And neither has the divorce and neither has the hairpiece.*"

"Yes, sir, I threw it at our legal types and, uh, they say it's illegal."

"*All right, so I'm research-inclined! Does that mean I'm not success-oriented? Does that mean I'm not profit-motivated?*"

"In my book, you just can't write off a country that doubles its razor-blade sales by getting people to shave with two blades at once."

"*Get your oars back in the cash flow!*"

"It's simple: We find new job roles for blacks, women, and Third World, humanize our assembly line, beef up wages and pensions, lower prices, improve quality and profits, and go home to bed."

"*And venture capital! Remember venture capital?*"

"It wasn't perfect, but I'll take 1968 any day. Your Dow's pushing a thousand, the ad game is printing money, I haven't met my first wife. . . ."

"Do you realize the '29 Class Notes are now only three pages from the beginning of Class Notes?"

"In these days, when it takes a great deal of money to live, I feel damn farsighted in having a great deal of money."

"You're at my favorite stage."

"They're changing English 45 to Communication Techniques 232,
Chaucer to Erica Jong, and me to tape."

"I've abated my pollution, racially diversified my personnel, and faced consumer advocates. Now she's calling for sideburns and a Fu Manchu mustache!"

"Freddy, let's not talk anymore about your mother—let's talk about the Bold Ruler filly she gave you."

"Come, Ninevah! Come, Tyre!"

"Oh, Porter. At your age, sixty-two isn't old."

"I'll tell you where I get my 'psychic income'—money!"

"Look, Marian, I've eschewed baldness!"

"The Depression, the game in the bowl, the war. Damn it, ours was the life."

"Something else I've always felt, Stanley. If you have a really great deal of money, it becomes physically impossible to get too big for your britches."

"This is my plan for the golden years: Stay smashed."

"Let's face it, Tom. A society that's paying its Frank Sinatras and Johnny Carsons more than its you's and me's is out of whack."